This Bellerophon Book has 31 figures from the Christian armies of the west (the Franks), 10 figures from the Byzantine Empire and central Europe—allies (some of the time) of the Franks, and 27 figures of their splendid Muslim foemen. You can deploy them over the same lands of the eastern Mediterranean that are embattled today. Mr. Nicolle, the celebrated scholar of ancient arms, has spared no efforts of research in making these figures authentic.

Fatimid Guardsman with Caliph's parasol-emblem
early 12th century

Flags, banners and other insignia were highly developed in early medieval Muslim times. The most important was often a decorative parasol, and that of the Fatimids was made of gold-embroidered white silk topped by two jewel-encrusted gold balls. The rider wears a segmented iron helmet and a richly decorated silk tunic. Sources: parasol, description by Ibn al T'uwayr, *Annales de l'Institut des Etudes Orientales,* Algiers, 1952; rider: Egyptian ceramic dish, No. 41.12, Freer Gallery, Washington D.C.

Bellerophon Books

Fatimid Daylamite infantryman
early 12th century

Daylamis from northern Iran served in many Muslim armies. Their national weapon was the *zhupin* javelin, used with long shields with flattened bases to form a shield-wall. A lamellar *jawshan* cuirass of cuir-bouilli hardened leather is worn here. Sources: paper fragments, Mus. of Islamic Art, Cairo; Al Sufi, MS Marsh 144, Bodleian Lib.

Bellerophon Books

Attach parasol to rider's stand

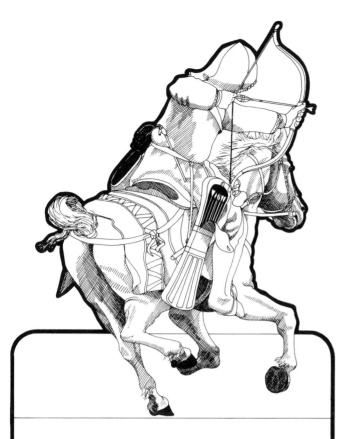

Saljuq turcoman tribesman, 11th - 12th centuries

Turkish nomad horse-archers formed the bulk of the first Saljuq armies. They possessed little armor and wore drab furs, felts and heavy woolen garments. Their saddle-cloths and bound-cane shields with bronze bosses would have been brightly colored. Sources: stone friezes from Daghestan; Hermitage, Louvre, Metropolitan Museum of Art.

Bellerophon Books

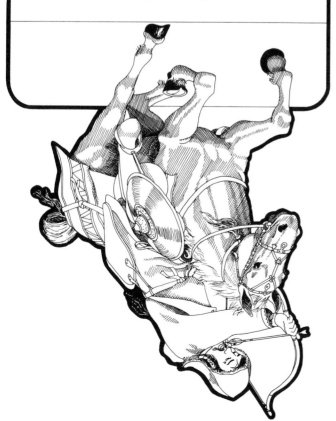

Aghovanian cavalryman from the southern Caucasus

Known to the First Crusade as *Agulani,* the Muslim horsemen of the Caucasus used equipment which mirrored both Arab and Iranian traditions. Their most characteristic protection was a heavy hauberk of iron scales. Sources: carvings of saints, West Front, Nicorzminda Church, Georgia, USSR; silver icons of St. George, from Georgia, Hermitage and Tbilisi Museum, USSR; bronze horse from Daghestan, Hermitage; fresco, Iprari Church, Georgia, USSR

Bellerophon Books

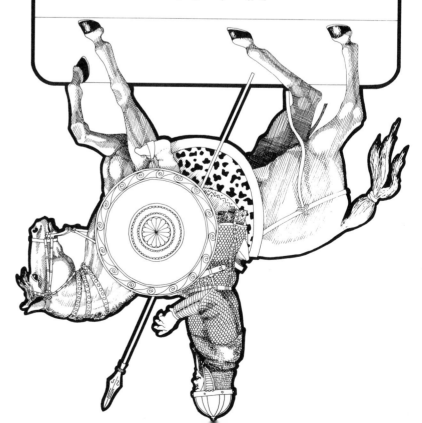

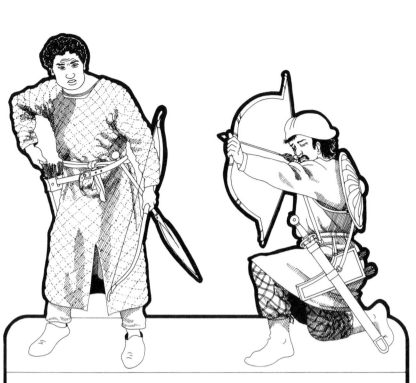

A Nubian archer & an Armenian-Fatimid archer
11th - 12th centuries

Standing: many Nubians and other Africans served in the Fatimid armies of Egypt. Their heavy quilted protective coats were typical of North Africa and the Sahara, but their large bows and asagai-type short spears seem to have been specifically Sudanese. Sources: Nativity sequence, fresco from Faras Cathedral, National Museum, Khartoum, Sudan; ceramic wallplaques from Sabra, Bardo Museum, Tunis, Tunisia

Kneeling: Armenian mercenaries, both Christian and Muslim, had long served in Egypt, and their numbers increased after the Byzantine occupation of Armenia in the eleventh century. This warrior wears no armor. His shield appears to be built up of segments and his trousers are of a tartan-like material. Source: Coptic Gospels, MS Copte 13, Bib. nationale, Paris

Bellerophon Books

Arab-Fatimid heavy cavalryman
11th-early 12th century

Armored cavalry, some riding armored horses, had long been known in the Muslim Middle East. This man wears a leather lamellar cuirass and a mail hauberk under a brightly colored tunic. His helmet is iron, whereas his horse's chamfron, or head protection, is of leather. Sources: Fatimid painted paper fragments, Kier Col., London; Coptic parchment, MS 581, Pierpont Morgan Library, N.Y.; Fatimid helmet, Hist. Mus., Kairouan

Bellerophon Books

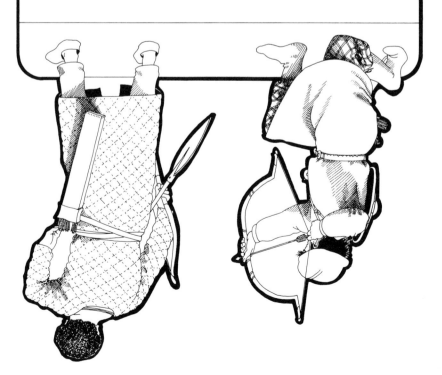

Norman knight, late 11th century

The mailed horsemen of northwestern France were the elite warriors of their day. Their horses, like their armor and shields, were large and heavy. This man has the neck and chin protection of his mail hauberk hanging loose, which could provide an alternative interpretation of some Normans in the Bayeux Tapestry, our source.

Bellerophon Books

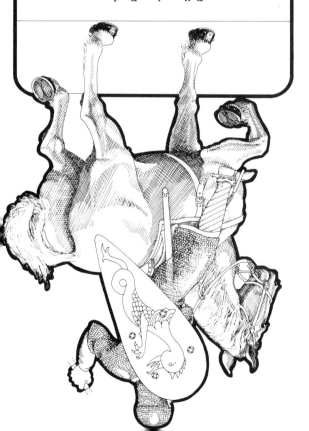

French infantryman
late 11th-early 12th century

Old-fashioned armor and weapons persisted among French infantry, esp. in poorer regions like the Massif Central, and included round shields and loose-necked hauberks. The helmet here probably is of a style of the late Roman Empire. Sources: capitals in St. Nectaire & in Autun Cathedral; chessmen, Bargello, Florence; tympanum, Vezelay.

Bellerophon Books

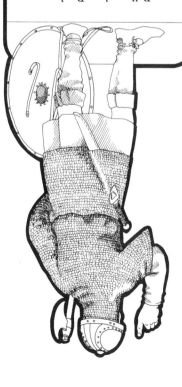

French monk, 11th century

Various churchmen accompanied the First Crusade, ranging from ambitious bishops to fanatical hermits. Source: *Moralia* from Citeau, Mun. Lib., Dijon

Bellerophon Books

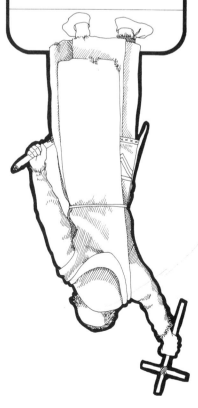

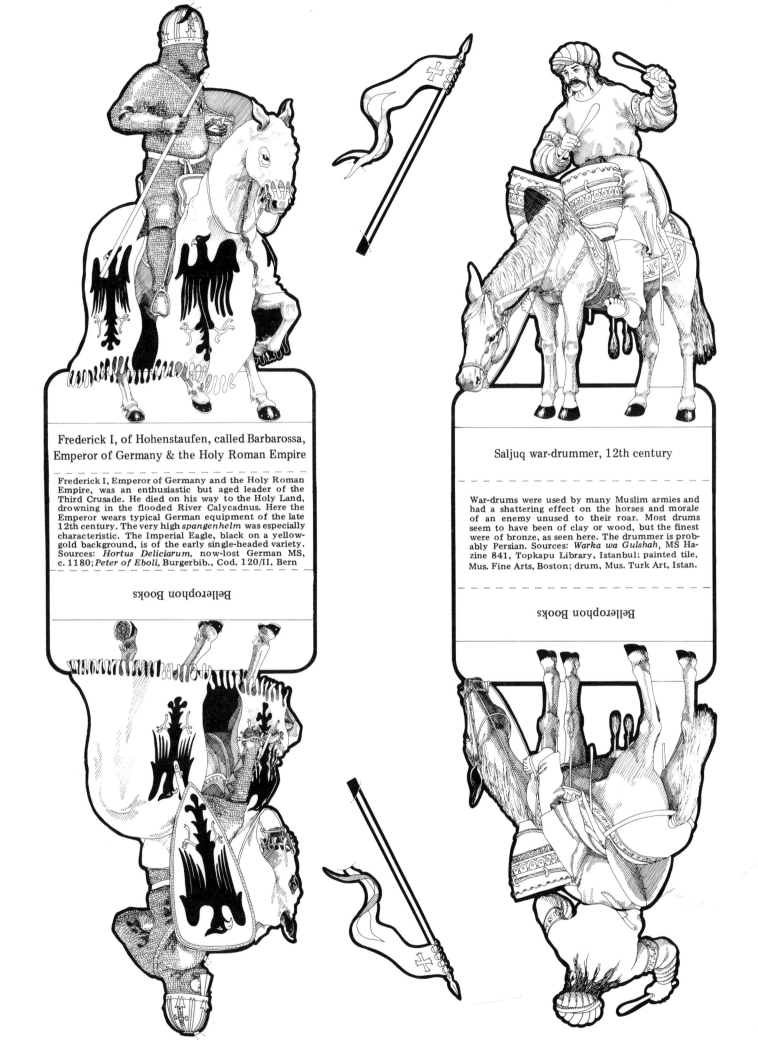

Frederick I, of Hohenstaufen, called Barbarossa, Emperor of Germany & the Holy Roman Empire

Frederick I, Emperor of Germany and the Holy Roman Empire, was an enthusiastic but aged leader of the Third Crusade. He died on his way to the Holy Land, drowning in the flooded River Calycadnus. Here the Emperor wears typical German equipment of the late 12th century. The very high *spangenhelm* was especially characteristic. The Imperial Eagle, black on a yellow-gold background, is of the early single-headed variety. Sources: *Hortus Deliciarum*, now-lost German MS, c. 1180; *Peter of Eboli*, Burgerbib., Cod. 120/II, Bern

Bellerophon Books

Saljuq war-drummer, 12th century

War-drums were used by many Muslim armies and had a shattering effect on the horses and morale of an enemy unused to their roar. Most drums seem to have been of clay or wood, but the finest were of bronze, as seen here. The drummer is probably Persian. Sources: *Warka wa Gulshah*, MS Hazine 841, Topkapu Library, Istanbul; painted tile, Mus. Fine Arts, Boston; drum, Mus. Turk Art, Istan.

Bellerophon Books

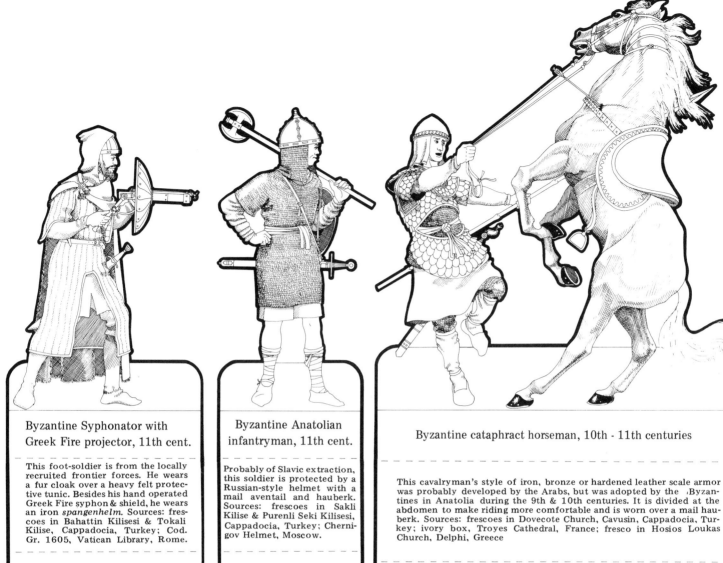

Byzantine Syphonator with Greek Fire projector, 11th cent.

This foot-soldier is from the locally recruited frontier forces. He wears a fur cloak over a heavy felt protective tunic. Besides his hand operated Greek Fire syphon & shield, he wears an iron *spangenhelm*. Sources: frescoes in Bahattin Kilisesi & Tokali Kilise, Cappadocia, Turkey; Cod. Gr. 1605, Vatican Library, Rome.

Bellerophon Books

Byzantine Anatolian infantryman, 11th cent.

Probably of Slavic extraction, this soldier is protected by a Russian-style helmet with a mail aventail and hauberk. Sources: frescoes in Sakli Kilise & Purenli Seki Kilisesi, Cappadocia, Turkey; Cherni-gov Helmet, Moscow.

Bellerophon Books

Byzantine cataphract horseman, 10th - 11th centuries

This cavalryman's style of iron, bronze or hardened leather scale armor was probably developed by the Arabs, but was adopted by the Byzantines in Anatolia during the 9th & 10th centuries. It is divided at the abdomen to make riding more comfortable and is worn over a mail hauberk. Sources: frescoes in Dovecote Church, Cavusin, Cappadocia, Turkey; ivory box, Troyes Cathedral, France; fresco in Hosios Loukas Church, Delphi, Greece

Bellerophon Books

Italo-Norman knight, First Crusade

Byzantine and Saracenic influences are clearly seen in the military equipment of Norman Italy and Sicily. This man's heavy hauberk of iron scales is one example. The early heraldic device on his shield and pennon might indicate that Italy was also ahead in this field as well. Sources: carving in San Nicola di Bari, Italy; ivory chessmen, Cab. des Medailles, Bib. nat., Paris; Vatican MS Lat. 1202, from Monte Cassino; Exultet Rolls, Casanatense Lib. MS 724.B1, Rome; Bib. nat., Paris, MS Nouv. Acq. 710

Bellerophon Books

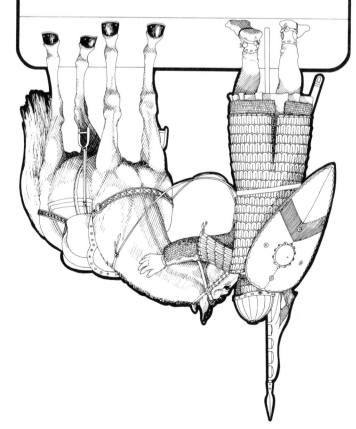

Provencal knight, First Crusade

Many of the horsemen of southern France, like those of Spain, seem to have equipped themselves more lightly than their northern allies. This man wears a heavy surcoat, perhaps of felt, over a padded gambeson, without apparent mail armor. Sources: capitals in the church of Ste. Foy, Conques, France; tomb of Dona Sancha, Benedictine Convent, Jaca, Spain; *Beatus of St. Sever,* MS Lat. 8878, Bib. nat., Paris

Bellerophon Books

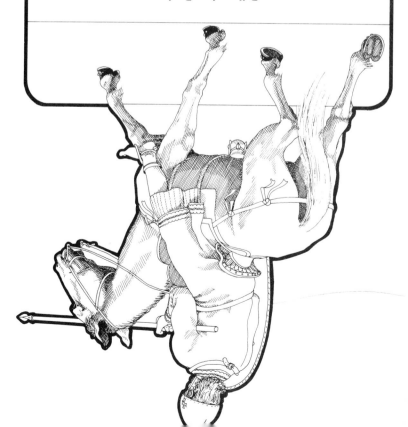

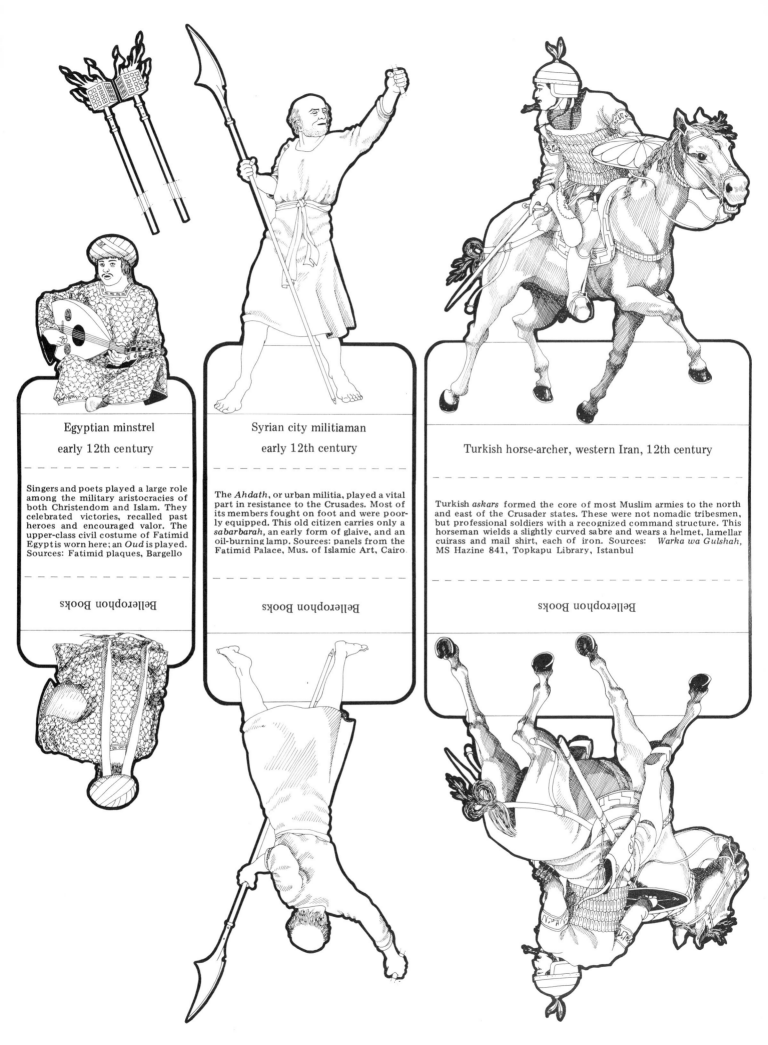

Egyptian minstrel
early 12th century

Singers and poets played a large role among the military aristocracies of both Christendom and Islam. They celebrated victories, recalled past heroes and encouraged valor. The upper-class civil costume of Fatimid Egypt is worn here; an *Oud* is played. Sources: Fatimid plaques, Bargello

Bellerophon Books

Syrian city militiaman
early 12th century

The *Ahdath*, or urban militia, played a vital part in resistance to the Crusades. Most of its members fought on foot and were poorly equipped. This old citizen carries only a *sabarbarah*, an early form of glaive, and an oil-burning lamp. Sources: panels from the Fatimid Palace, Mus. of Islamic Art, Cairo.

Bellerophon Books

Turkish horse-archer, western Iran, 12th century

Turkish *askars* formed the core of most Muslim armies to the north and east of the Crusader states. These were not nomadic tribesmen, but professional soldiers with a recognized command structure. This horseman wields a slightly curved sabre and wears a helmet, lamellar cuirass and mail shirt, each of iron. Sources: *Warka wa Gulshah*, MS Hazine 841, Topkapu Library, Istanbul

Bellerophon Books

Southern European infantry archer, mid-12th century

Having no horse-archers of their own, Crusader forces at first relied on infantry archers to keep their Turkish foes at a distance. This man draws a simple form of composite bow and wears a sleeveless mail jerkin that does not hinder his arms. Sources: relief in St. Giles du Gard, France; candelabrum, San Paolo fuori la Mura, Rome; font, San Frediano, Lucca; chessman, Bargello

Bellerophon Books

Crusader mailed infantry, Italian style, mid-12th century

The adoption of fixed visors probably reflected an increased danger from arrows in 12th century warfare. The slits in the sides of the mail hauberk here show this to be an infantryman, as does the single mail protection for his left leg, placed forward when fighting behind a shield-wall. Sources: facade, Verona Cathedral & San Zeno

Bellerophon Books

Local infantry, Crusader States, mid-12th century

Syrian Christians, Armenians, & Maronites from Mt. Lebanon were recruited by the Crusader States. This infantry archer has a composite bow, an iron helmet of European form, and a light leather shield. Sources: Queen Melisende's Psalter, MS Egerton 1139, Brit. Lib.; capitals, Nazareth Mus.

overlap here

Bellerophon Books

Templar knight, mid 12th-century

Scale armor was less popular than mail in western Europe, but it was used, esp. in the south and most often during siege warfare. This Templar wears the white surcoat with a red cross as a mark of his Order and carries the *Beau Seant* black-and-white banner of the Templars. Sources: facade, St. Giles du Gard; capitals, La Madeleine, Vezelay

Bellerophon Books

Mesopotamian horseman, mid-12th century

Lightly armed as he is, this Turkish *mamluk* is probably equipped for reconnaissance rather than battle. His iron helmet is a highly decorated *spangenhelm,* while his shield is formed from a spiral of cane bound together with silk thread behind a decorated bronze boss. Sources: ceramic warrior figure, Nat. Mus., Damascus; altar-arch, Monastery church of Mar Hudeni, Mosul, Iraq; MS Ahmad III 3494, Sulaymaniye Lib., Istanbul

Bellerophon Books

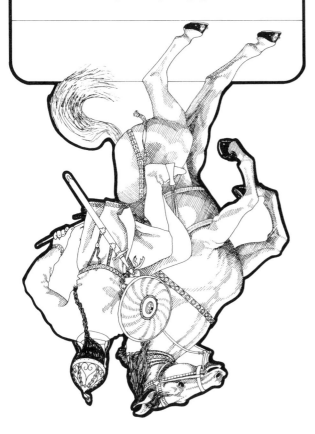

Caliph's bodyguard, Iraq, & Persian heavy cavalryman
12th century

The standing man is unarmored and wears ceremonial costume of very rich fabric. His boots, perhaps of red leather, are similarly decorated. Even his spear is more of a ceremonial insignia, perhaps being an *anazah* which was used as a mark of rank in Bagdad. Sources: *Al Hariri,* MSS Arabe 5847 & 6094, Bib. nat., Paris; MS Essad Effendi 2916, Sulaymaniye Lib., Istanbul
The traditional mounted warrior of the Iranian regions was a lancer and swordsman rather than a horse-archer. This man wears a cloth over his helmet and has mail sleeves that are separate, fastened over his hardened-leather lamellar cuirass. His wooden shield is covered with painted leather. Sources: stucco panel from Iran, Seattle Art Museum; Iranian mirror, Louvre

Bellerophon Books

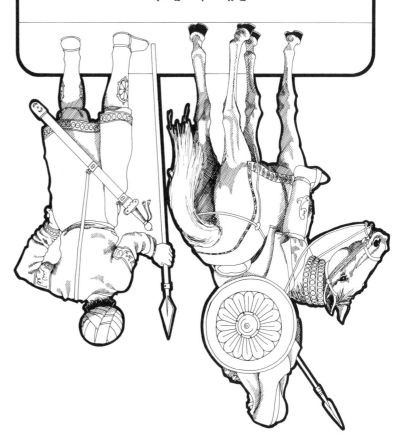

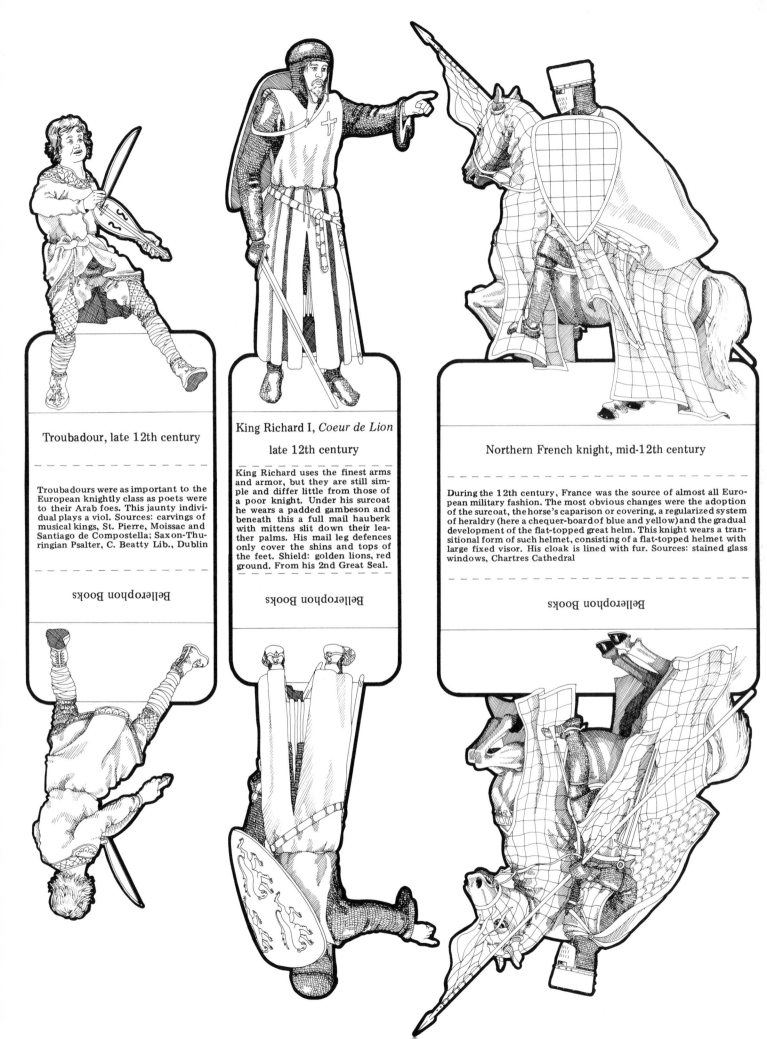

Troubadour, late 12th century

Troubadours were as important to the European knightly class as poets were to their Arab foes. This jaunty individual plays a viol. Sources: carvings of musical kings, St. Pierre, Moissac and Santiago de Compostella; Saxon-Thuringian Psalter, C. Beatty Lib., Dublin

Bellerophon Books

King Richard I, *Coeur de Lion*

late 12th century

King Richard uses the finest arms and armor, but they are still simple and differ little from those of a poor knight. Under his surcoat he wears a padded gambeson and beneath this a full mail hauberk with mittens slit down their leather palms. His mail leg defences only cover the shins and tops of the feet. Shield: golden lions, red ground. From his 2nd Great Seal.

Bellerophon Books

Northern French knight, mid-12th century

During the 12th century, France was the source of almost all European military fashion. The most obvious changes were the adoption of the surcoat, the horse's caparison or covering, a regularized system of heraldry (here a chequer-board of blue and yellow) and the gradual development of the flat-topped great helm. This knight wears a transitional form of such helmet, consisting of a flat-topped helmet with large fixed visor. His cloak is lined with fur. Sources: stained glass windows, Chartres Cathedral

Bellerophon Books

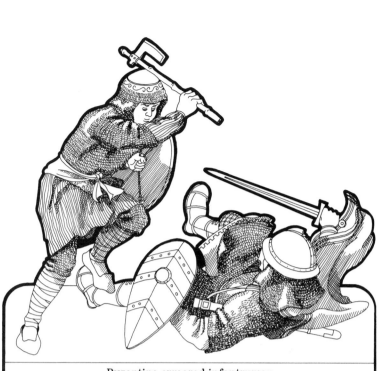

Byzantine armored infantryman
& a Muslim Anatolian infantryman
12th century

Top: infantry played an increasingly important role in the new Turkish Saljuq states in Anatolia. Most were probably locally recruited. This man wears mail chausses over his legs in addition to his hauberk. His axe is of a traditional Anatolian form but the emblem on his shield, from a late Saljuq carving, is of the ancient Animal Style traditional to the Eurasian steppes. Sources: frescoes in Karanlik Kilise, Goreme, Kirkdam alte Kilise, Peristrema valley, Turkey
Bottom: western European military fashions seem to have had strong influence in Byzantium from the 12th cent. onwards. This man wears a helmet called a kettle-hat; his kite-shaped shield is typically Byzantine. Sources: MS Grec 806, Bib. nat., Paris; MS 463, Iviron Monas. Lib., Mt. Athos, Greece

Bellerophon Books

Byzantine guards officer
12th century

Elite troops in Constantinople continued to wear uniforms directly descended from late Roman styles. This man has a Ukrainian helmet of Byzantine inspiration with a cloth-covered mail aventail. Under his silk-covered quilted jerkin is a mail hauberk, and he is armed with mace and sword. Sources: helmet, Byzantine dishes from Beryozovo and Bazilevsky Col., Hermitage, USSR

Bellerophon Books

Infantry archer, 12th cent.
E. Anatolia or W. Iran

Mountain peasants south of the Caucasus range used simple rather than composite bows of the Central Asian type. Sources: Homberg Ewer from Mosul, Kofler Col., Lucerne; Syriac Gospels, MS Add. 7170, British Library

Bellerophon Books

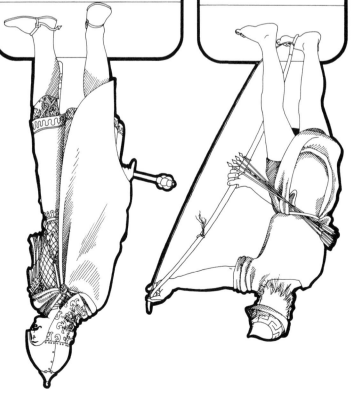

The Byzantine Emperor Manuel Comnenus and his wife, Maria of Antioch. 12th century

Byzantine Imperial Court Costume was probably the most magnificent to be seen anywhere in the Middle Ages, as it used huge amounts of gold, pearls and precious stones. The Emperor Manuel I Comnenus favored the Crusaders and fought hard against the Turks in Asia Minor and even married a Crusader Princess, Maria of Antioch. Source: Vatican Library Cod. Gr. 1176

King Louis VII of France & a southern French infantryman. 12th century

Louis VII was a leading spirit behind the disastrous Second Crusade, which collapsed before the walls of Damascus. Here he wears a rich surcoat, decorated with the lilies of France on a blue field, over his mail hauberk. The foot soldier wears the sort of short hauberk of scale armor apparently worn by many poorer soldiers, especially those from southern France or Italy. Sources: stained glass windows, Chartres Cathedral, 12th century; carvings from Notre Dame de la Couldre, 12th century, Isabella Stewart Gardner Museum, Boston; carving of Goliath, St. Giles du Gard, 12th cent.

Bellerophon Books

Bellerophon Books

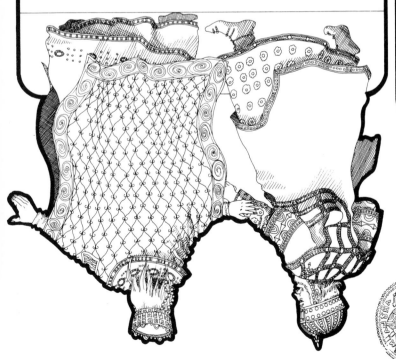

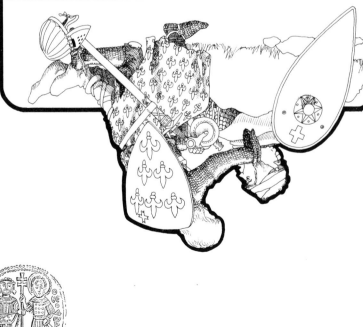

Coin of Manuel

Sicilian Norman heavy infantry, 12th century

In many ways Sicilian military styles differed from those of the rest of Europe, but this man's equipment is relatively standard. His helmet has a fixed visor while his shield has metal reinforcing strips. Sources: capitals, Monreale Cathedral; frieze, La Martorana, Palermo

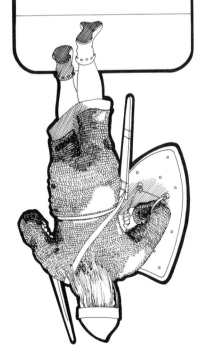

Sicilian Muslim infantry guardsman, 12th century

Muslims formed guard units to protect the ruler and his Treasury in Norman Sicily. Here is a mixture of Arab and Byzantine styles. A cloth is wound around his helmet, his cuirass is formed of iron scales joined by leather straps, & the shield has a rivetted metal plate. Source: Monreale Cathedral

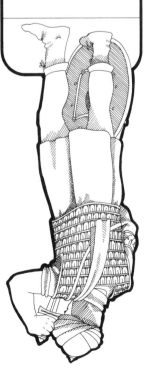

Italian crossbowman Norman Sicily late 12th century

The forces of Norman Sicily were very mixed. This infantryman is an Italian and he wears an early form of sallet. His crossbow is also of an early type without a stirrup. Sources: *Liber ad honorem augusti*, Sicilian MS Cod. 120, Burgerbibliothek, Bern; capitals in Monreale Cathedral, Italy

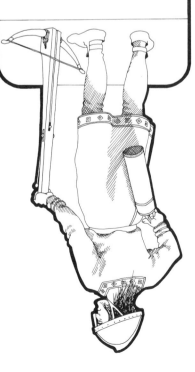

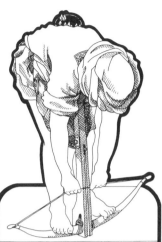

Muslim crossbowman Norman Sicily late 12th century

Muslims formed the professional backbone and most loyal element in the armies of Norman Sicily. This man is loading an early form of crossbow by holding it down with both feet as he pulls back the cord. Sources: MS Cod. 120, Burgerbibliothek, Bern; capitals, Monreale Cathed.

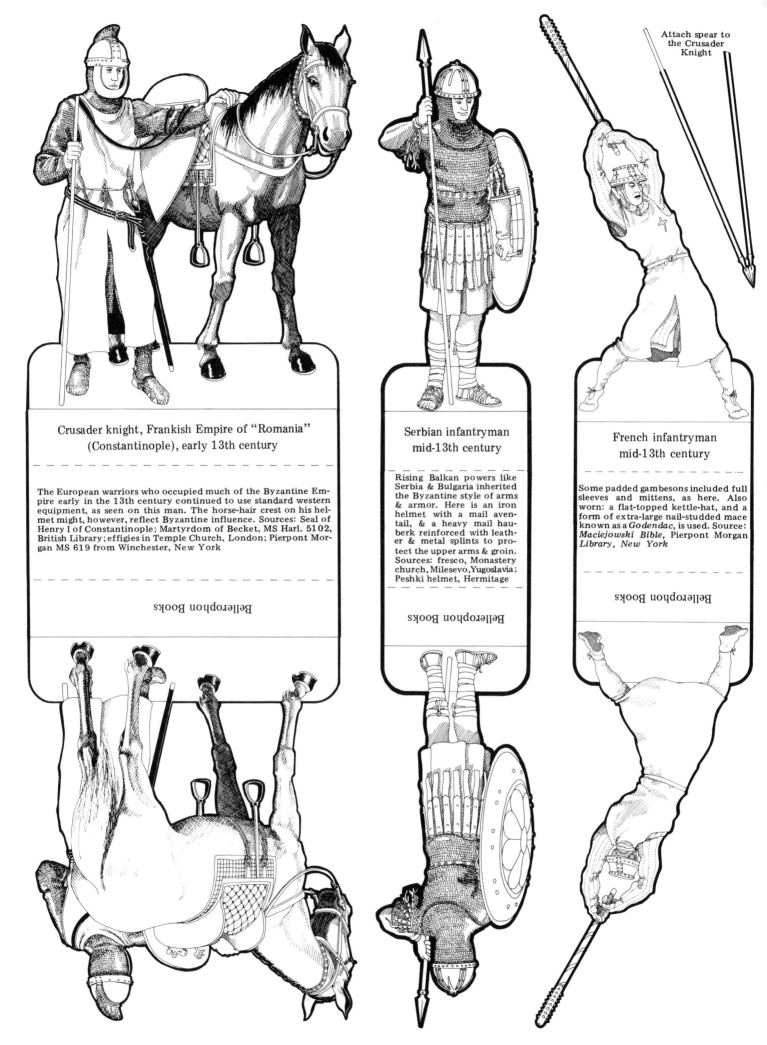

Attach spear to the Crusader Knight

Crusader knight, Frankish Empire of "Romania" (Constantinople), early 13th century

The European warriors who occupied much of the Byzantine Empire early in the 13th century continued to use standard western equipment, as seen on this man. The horse-hair crest on his helmet might, however, reflect Byzantine influence. Sources: Seal of Henry I of Constantinople; Martyrdom of Becket, MS Harl. 5102, British Library; effigies in Temple Church, London; Pierpont Morgan MS 619 from Winchester, New York

Bellerophon Books

Serbian infantryman mid-13th century

Rising Balkan powers like Serbia & Bulgaria inherited the Byzantine style of arms & armor. Here is an iron helmet with a mail aventail, & a heavy mail hauberk reinforced with leather & metal splints to protect the upper arms & groin. Sources: fresco, Monastery church, Milesevo, Yugoslavia; Peshki helmet, Hermitage

Bellerophon Books

French infantryman mid-13th century

Some padded gambesons included full sleeves and mittens, as here. Also worn: a flat-topped kettle-hat, and a form of extra-large nail-studded mace known as a *Godendac*, is used. Source: *Maciejowski Bible*, Pierpont Morgan Library, New York

Bellerophon Books

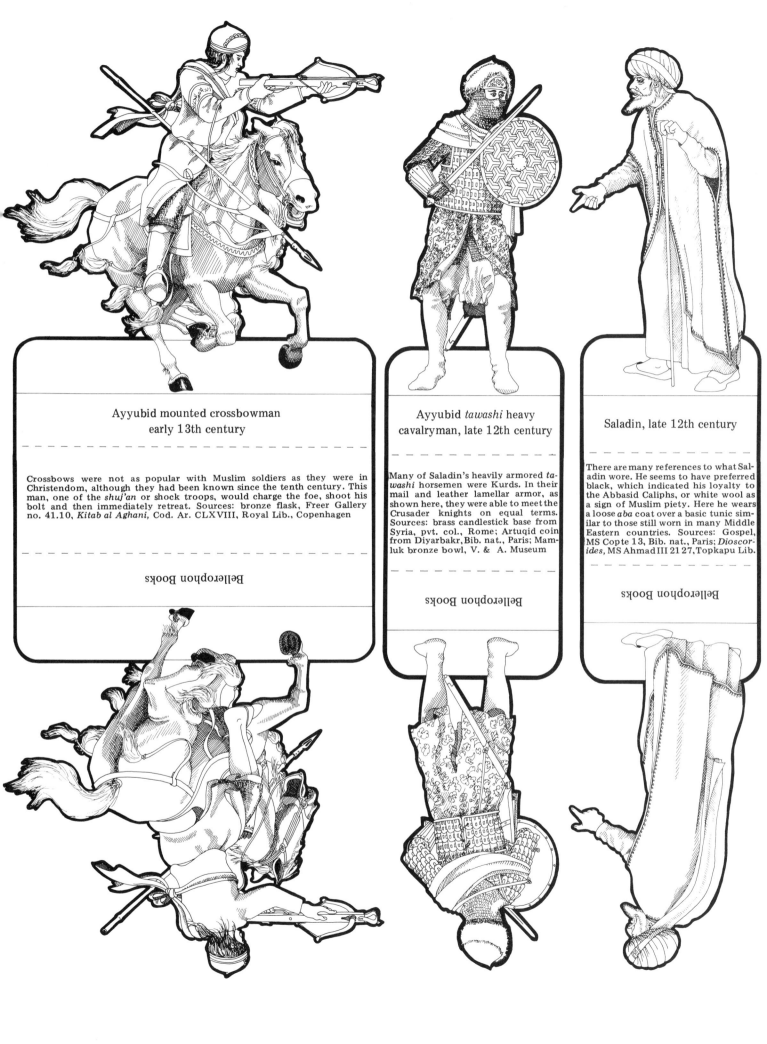

Ayyubid mounted crossbowman
early 13th century

Crossbows were not as popular with Muslim soldiers as they were in Christendom, although they had been known since the tenth century. This man, one of the *shuj'an* or shock troops, would charge the foe, shoot his bolt and then immediately retreat. Sources: bronze flask, Freer Gallery no. 41.10, *Kitab al Aghani,* Cod. Ar. CLXVIII, Royal Lib., Copenhagen

Bellerophon Books

Ayyubid *tawashi* heavy
cavalryman, late 12th century

Many of Saladin's heavily armored *ta-washi* horsemen were Kurds. In their mail and leather lamellar armor, as shown here, they were able to meet the Crusader knights on equal terms. Sources: brass candlestick base from Syria, pvt. col., Rome; Artuqid coin from Diyarbakr, Bib. nat., Paris; Mamluk bronze bowl, V. & A. Museum

Bellerophon Books

Saladin, late 12th century

There are many references to what Saladin wore. He seems to have preferred black, which indicated his loyalty to the Abbasid Caliphs, or white wool as a sign of Muslim piety. Here he wears a loose *aba* coat over a basic tunic similar to those still worn in many Middle Eastern countries. Sources: Gospel, MS Copte 13, Bib. nat., Paris; *Dioscorides,* MS Ahmad III 21 27, Topkapu Lib.

Bellerophon Books

Left: French infantryman
Right: Infantryman from the Crusader Kingdom of Acre
13th century

Kneeling: infantry became increasingly important in the 13th century, as most
warfare consisted largely of sieges. This man has an iron kettle-hat form of helmet to be worn over a padded arming cap. His gambeson or protective tunic is also quilted as are his chausses or thigh defences. Such a gambeson could be worn
on its own although it normally formed a padded layer beneath other armor.
Source: *Maciejowski Bible*, Pierpont Morgan Library, N.Y.; Standing: the reduced
Crusader states prolonged their survival by relying on massive fortifications garri-
soned by well-equipped infantry. This man wears a small painted helmet and a
full mail hauberk plus separate leg protections. The dagger at his belt probably re-
flects Italian influence. Source: *William of Tyre*, MS 562, Municipal Lib., Dijon

Bellerophon Books

Hospitaler Turcopole, mid-13th century

Turcopoles are still a bit of a mystery. At first they may have been local
Christians, plus even some Muslims. They certainly did not normally fight
in the style of Turkish horse-archers, though the mounted archers in their
ranks may have operated like Byzantine horse-archers. This man's shield
and lance-pennon bear a white cross on a red background, while his black
cloak would also have had a white cross on the left breast. Sources: Icon
of St. George, St. Catherine's Monastery, Sinai, Egypt; *History of William
of Tyre*, MS Pal. Lat. 1963, Vatican Library

Bellerophon Books

Templar knight and sergeant, late 13th century

Templar seals show two men riding one horse. As a symbol of poverty it was probably rooted in legend. But the concept of increasing an army's speed by making horsemen carry foot-soldiers to battle was real enough and had been common practice in Muslim Syria for several centuries. Here the knight wears the white active service cloak of his Order and wields a heavy single-edged falchion. The sergeant wears a brown active service cloak and carries the knight's great helm, which is a transitional form with a slightly domed crown. His own helmet is a very early sallet and he is armed with a short-hafted glaive. Sources: knight, effigy of Robert of Normandy, Gloucester Cathedral; MS Harley 782, British Library; sergeant, altar panel, Pistoia Cathedral, Italy; *Apocalypse of St. John,* British Library

Bellerophon Books

Italian knight, late 13th century

Italy was to become one of the main armor producing centers of the later Middle Ages. Even by the 13th century equipment in Italy often seems to have been more advanced than elsewhere. This man's helmet has a light wooden crest and an early form of hinged visor. His limbs are protected by pieces of richly decorated hardened leather, perhaps reflecting close contact with the eastern Mediterranean. His coat of arms is also unusual. Sources: frescoes in San Gimignano; relief on tomb of Guillaume Balnis, Convent of the Annunziata, Florence

Bellerophon Books

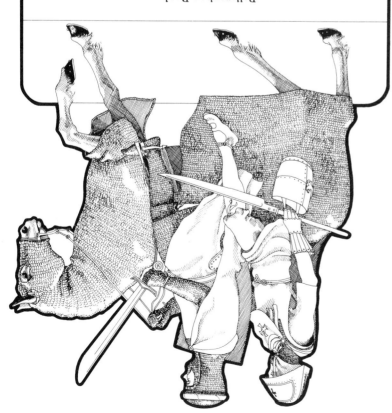

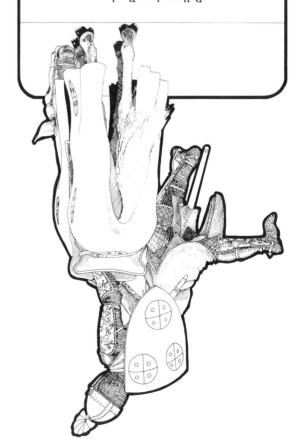

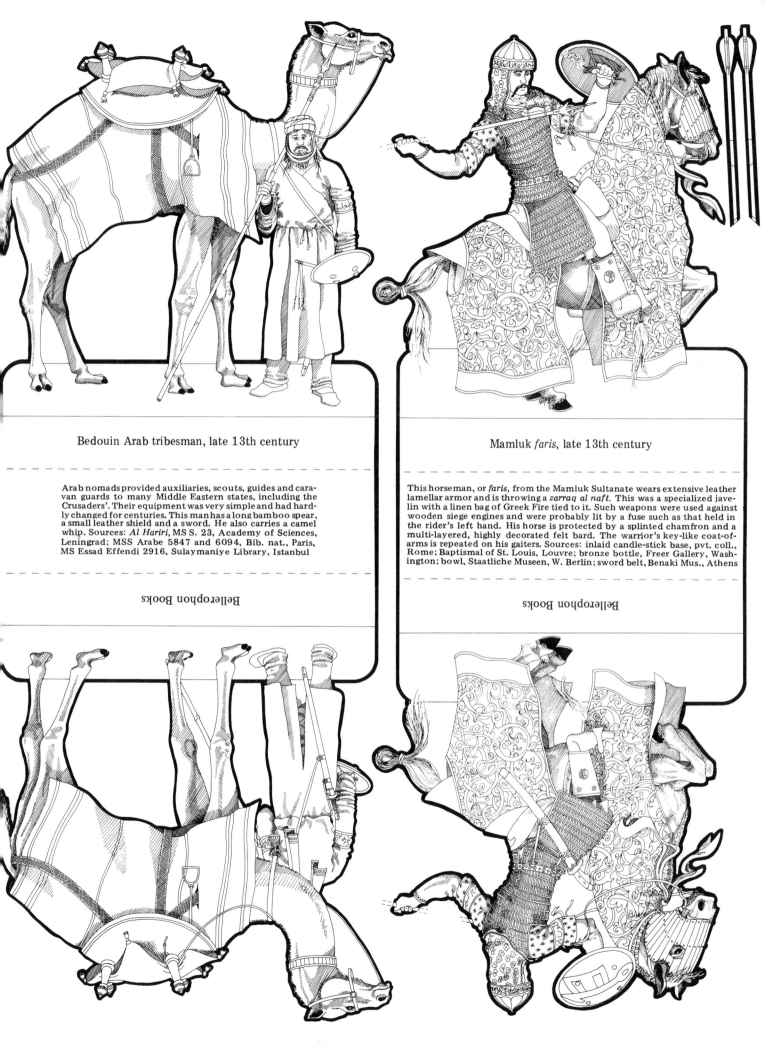

Bedouin Arab tribesman, late 13th century

Arab nomads provided auxiliaries, scouts, guides and caravan guards to many Middle Eastern states, including the Crusaders'. Their equipment was very simple and had hardly changed for centuries. This man has a long bamboo spear, a small leather shield and a sword. He also carries a camel whip. Sources: *Al Hariri*, MS S. 23, Academy of Sciences, Leningrad; MSS Arabe 5847 and 6094, Bib. nat., Paris, MS Essad Effendi 2916, Sulaymaniye Library, Istanbul

Bellerophon Books

Mamluk *faris*, late 13th century

This horseman, or *faris*, from the Mamluk Sultanate wears extensive leather lamellar armor and is throwing a *zarraq al naft*. This was a specialized javelin with a linen bag of Greek Fire tied to it. Such weapons were used against wooden siege engines and were probably lit by a fuse such as that held in the rider's left hand. His horse is protected by a splinted chamfron and a multi-layered, highly decorated felt bard. The warrior's key-like coat-of-arms is repeated on his gaiters. Sources: inlaid candle-stick base, pvt. coll., Rome; Baptismal of St. Louis, Louvre; bronze bottle, Freer Gallery, Washington; bowl, Staatliche Museen, W. Berlin; sword belt, Benaki Mus., Athens

Bellerophon Books

Crusader knight, mid-13th century

This horseman is armored in purely European style, although some decorative features such as the streamers in his helmet, his small banner and his horse's rich caparison, seem to have been fashions in the Crusader states. His coat-of-arms is red and white with a blue cadency mark, or bar, drawn across. Sources: statues on west front, Wells Cathedral; ceramic fragment from Al Mina, Historical Museum, Antakya, Turkey; *William of Tyre*, MS Pal. Lat. 1063, Vatican Library; MS 562, Municipal Library, Dijon

Bellerophon Books

English knight, late 13th century

The second half of the 13th century saw many developments in European armor. This Englishman wears the new, conical great helm which gave a glancing surface to a blow. The aillettes on his shoulders seem to have been largely decorative. Sources: effigy in Gosberton church; brass in Trumpington church

Bellerophon Books

German knight armed for foot combat, late 13th century

The Germans were widely known as excellent foot soldiers while the French were considered better on horseback. This knight wears a separate mail coif and a mail hauberk. Between these he has an early version of the coat-of-plates in which strips of metal or hardened leather are rivetted inside a heavy surcoat. Sources: *St. Maurice*, Magdeburg Cathedral; capital, Constance

Bellerophon Books

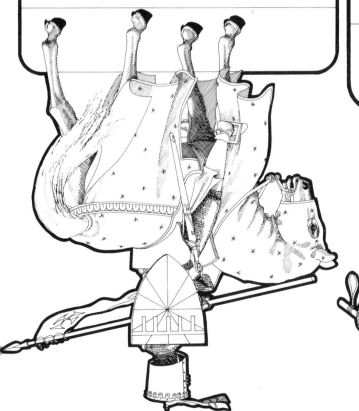

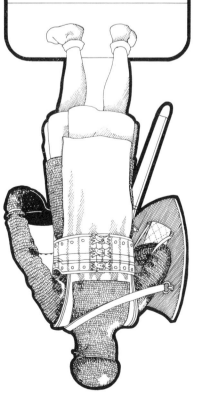

West Iranian heavy cavalryman
late 13th-early 14th century

Native Iranian arms and armor did not change immediately after the Mongol conquest and traditional styles persisted for several generations. This horseman wears aventail, arm defenses and cuirass, each of iron lamellae. His decorated lower arm defences, or vambraces, are of iron. The horse's armor, both the rigid chamfron and the lamellar bard, are of leather. Sources: *Kitab-i Samak Ayyar,* MS Ousley 381, Bodleian Lib., cauldron, Dahlem Museum

Bellerophon Books

Abbasid standard-bearer, mid-13th century

Black was the mark of the Abbasid Caliphs of Bagdad, and many of their banners were trimmed with this color. Muslim flags also appeared in a greater variety of shapes than did those of their Christian foes. Sources: *Al Hariri,* MS Arabe 5847, Bib. nat., Paris, and MS Essad Effendi 2916, Sulaymaniye Lib., Istanbul; sword of Caliph Mustasim Billah, Topkapu Armory, Istanbul; carved gateway, Amadiya, Iraq, recently collapsed

Bellerophon Books

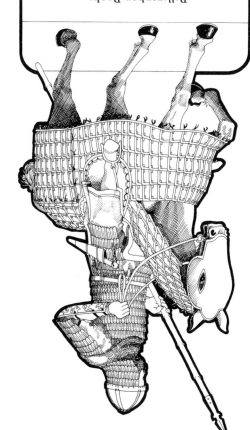

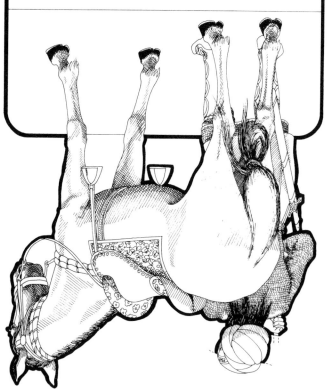

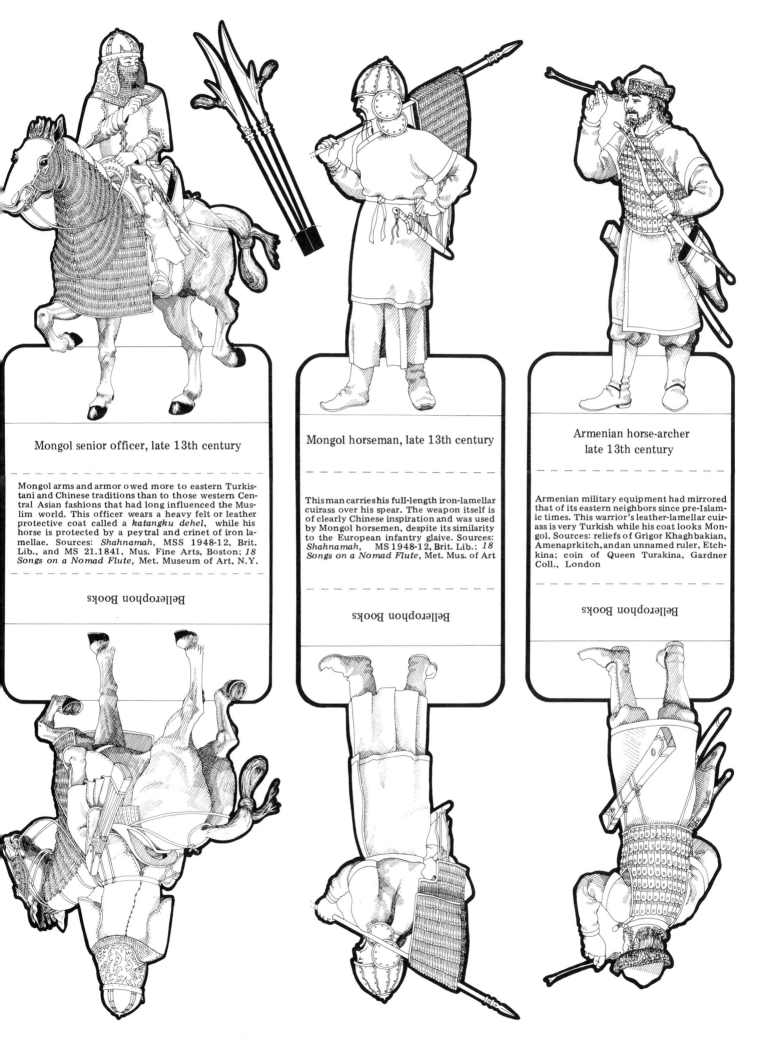

Mongol senior officer, late 13th century

Mongol arms and armor owed more to eastern Turkistani and Chinese traditions than to those western Central Asian fashions that had long influenced the Muslim world. This officer wears a heavy felt or leather protective coat called a *katangku dehel,* while his horse is protected by a peytral and crinet of iron lamellae. Sources: *Shahnamah,* MSS 1948-12, Brit. Lib., and MS 21.1841, Mus. Fine Arts, Boston; *18 Songs on a Nomad Flute,* Met. Museum of Art, N.Y.

Bellerophon Books

Mongol horseman, late 13th century

This man carries his full-length iron-lamellar cuirass over his spear. The weapon itself is of clearly Chinese inspiration and was used by Mongol horsemen, despite its similarity to the European infantry glaive. Sources: *Shahnamah,* MS 1948-12, Brit. Lib.; *18 Songs on a Nomad Flute,* Met. Mus. of Art

Bellerophon Books

Armenian horse-archer late 13th century

Armenian military equipment had mirrored that of its eastern neighbors since pre-Islamic times. This warrior's leather-lamellar cuirass is very Turkish while his coat looks Mongol. Sources: reliefs of Grigor Khaghbakian, Amenaprkitch, and an unnamed ruler, Etchkina; coin of Queen Turakina, Gardner Coll., London

Bellerophon Books

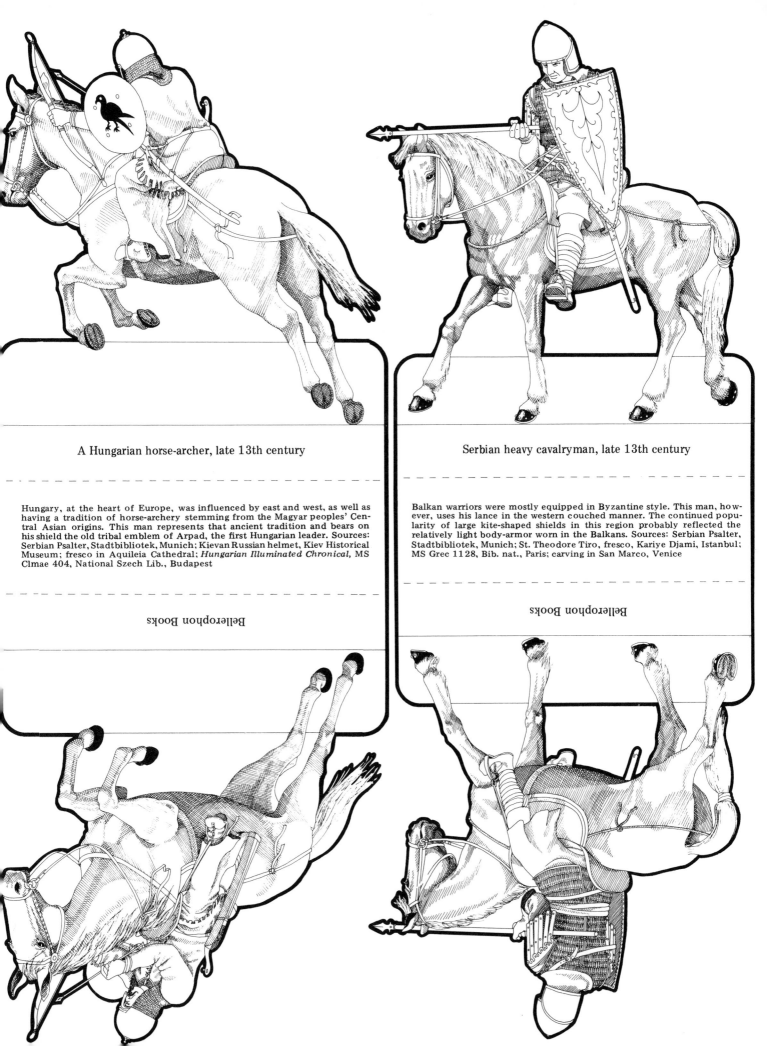

A Hungarian horse-archer, late 13th century

Hungary, at the heart of Europe, was influenced by east and west, as well as having a tradition of horse-archery stemming from the Magyar peoples' Central Asian origins. This man represents that ancient tradition and bears on his shield the old tribal emblem of Arpad, the first Hungarian leader. Sources: Serbian Psalter, Stadtbibliotek, Munich; Kievan Russian helmet, Kiev Historical Museum; fresco in Aquileia Cathedral; *Hungarian Illuminated Chronical*, MS Clmae 404, National Szech Lib., Budapest

Bellerophon Books

Serbian heavy cavalryman, late 13th century

Balkan warriors were mostly equipped in Byzantine style. This man, however, uses his lance in the western couched manner. The continued popularity of large kite-shaped shields in this region probably reflected the relatively light body-armor worn in the Balkans. Sources: Serbian Psalter, Stadtbibliotek, Munich; St. Theodore Tiro, fresco, Kariye Djami, Istanbul; MS Grec 1128, Bib. nat., Paris; carving in San Marco, Venice

Bellerophon Books

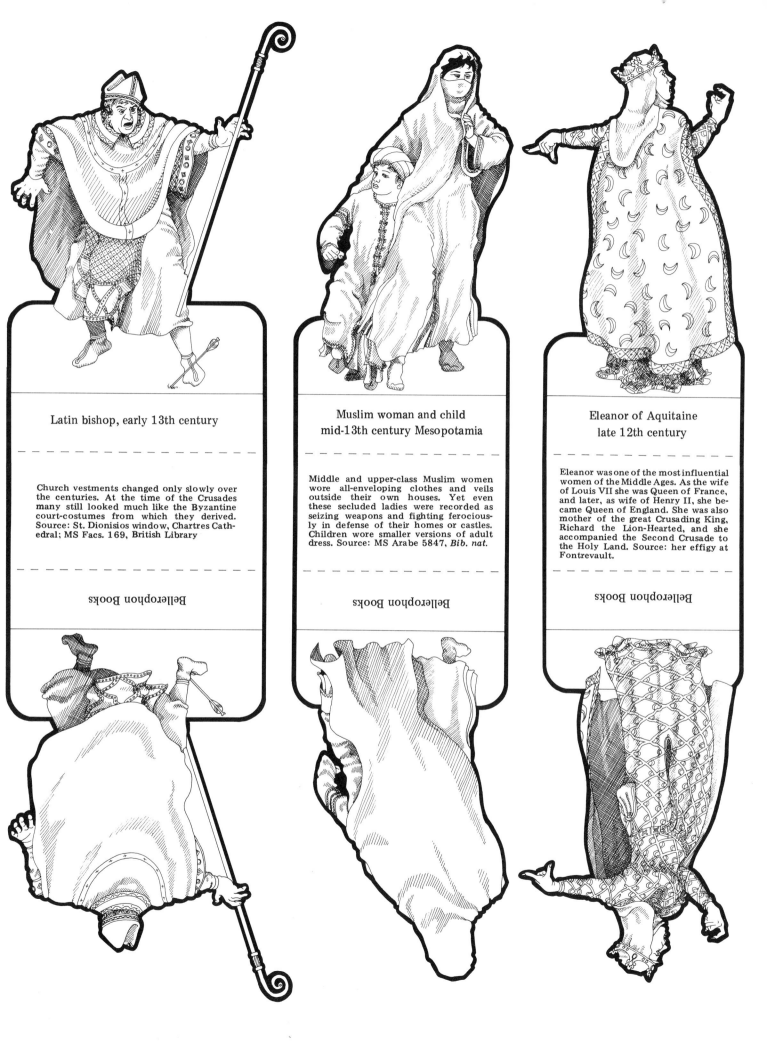

Latin bishop, early 13th century

Church vestments changed only slowly over the centuries. At the time of the Crusades many still looked much like the Byzantine court-costumes from which they derived. Source: St. Dionisios window, Chartres Cathedral; MS Facs. 169, British Library

Bellerophon Books

Muslim woman and child
mid-13th century Mesopotamia

Middle and upper-class Muslim women wore all-enveloping clothes and veils outside their own houses. Yet even these secluded ladies were recorded as seizing weapons and fighting ferociously in defense of their homes or castles. Children wore smaller versions of adult dress. Source: MS Arabe 5847, *Bib. nat.*

Bellerophon Books

Eleanor of Aquitaine
late 12th century

Eleanor was one of the most influential women of the Middle Ages. As the wife of Louis VII she was Queen of France, and later, as wife of Henry II, she became Queen of England. She was also mother of the great Crusading King, Richard the Lion-Hearted, and she accompanied the Second Crusade to the Holy Land. Source: her effigy at Fontrevault.

Bellerophon Books